# Crocodile
## ride

www.autumnchildrensbooks.co.uk

Crocodile said to his wife one night,
"Will you come with me in this bright moonlight
on our brand new bikes for a nine mile ride?"
"All right," said his bride, but she turned and sighed

"At this time of night, a ride on a bike isn't quite what I would really like."

Croc just smil_e_d and said, "Let's try.
You'll f_i_nd these b_i_k_e_s can really fly!"

Off down the hill they began to gl_i_d_e_.
"You see," said Croc, "it's a very f_i_n_e_ r_i_d_e_.
Be glad that you took my adv_i_ce_.
A h_i_k_e_ on a b_i_k_e_ is really n_i_ce_."

His wife replied, "Take my advice,
or you may have to pay the price.
Put your glasses on, if you don't mind.
Without them you are almost blind!"

Too late! Croc got an awful fright.

At the bottom of the hill, he didn't turn <u>right</u>!

# Newt's
## flute

In the light of the m<u>oo</u>n, one night in J<u>u</u>n<u>e</u>,
N<u>ew</u>t got out a <u>fl</u>ut<u>e</u> and bl<u>ew</u> out a t<u>u</u>n<u>e</u>.

Shrew said, "It's late, and I'm not in the m<u>oo</u>d.
T<u>o</u> play a t<u>u</u>n<u>e</u> at night is really very r<u>u</u>d<u>e</u>!
I was trying t<u>o</u> sn<u>oo</u>ze. Now I'm starting t<u>o</u> f<u>u</u>m<u>e</u>!"
And he jumped up and sc<u>oo</u>ted out of his r<u>oo</u>m.

"Listen, Newt!" he said. "I don't wish to argue,
but there's something I think it's time that you knew
Newts that play the flute well are truly very few,
and those newts really do not include you!"

Newt began to fume and he said, "That isn't fair!
But to tell you the truth, I really do not care!"
And he blew on his flute and played a new tune.
Shrew zoomed off, saying, "I'll be back very soon."

He fetched a h<u>uge</u> t<u>ube</u> and he bl<u>ew</u> 'toot, toot!'
"I can be as r<u>ude</u> as <u>you</u>," he said t<u>o</u> the n<u>ew</u>t.

Then Owl swooped down and said, "What I will do, is to take that flute and that tube from you."

And so, very soon, there was no more tune
and Owl could snooze in the light of the moon.

# Snake's
## cake

Snail made up his mind that he would make
a birthday cake for his best mate, Snake.
But Snail, I'm afraid, was a little bit lazy
and, some would say, a little bit crazy!

He laid up a tray with a cup and a plate,
"I aim to surprise Snake — I really can't wait!
I'll give this cake an amazing taste.
Let's take a look here — there's no time to waste."

"That's <u>a</u> p<u>ai</u>n," he said, as he c<u>a</u>m<u>e</u> to the p<u>a</u>g<u>e</u>.
"If I m<u>a</u>k<u>e</u> it like that, it will t<u>a</u>k<u>e</u> me an <u>a</u>g<u>e</u>.
I'll have to r<u>a</u>c<u>e</u> to the shops if I do what they s<u>ay</u>.
I'll just m<u>a</u>k<u>e</u> this c<u>a</u>k<u>e</u> in my very own w<u>ay</u>."

So in went some d<u>a</u>t<u>e</u>s and some st<u>a</u>l<u>e</u> cornfl<u>a</u>k<u>e</u>s.
Then Sn<u>ai</u>l g<u>a</u>v<u>e</u> the mix <u>a</u> few really good sh<u>a</u>k<u>e</u>s.
"I'll put in some gr<u>a</u>p<u>e</u>s, if there's any sp<u>a</u>c<u>e</u>,"
said that cr<u>a</u>zy Sn<u>ai</u>l, with <u>a</u> smile on his f<u>a</u>c<u>e</u>.

When Snake came, Snail placed the tray on the tabl

"Eat the whole cake, mate," said Snail, "if you're abl

I made it to wish you a 'Happy Birthday'.

I'm sure it will taste good. What do you say?"

"I'm wondering why you m<u>a</u>d<u>e</u> this c<u>a</u>k<u>e</u> tod<u>ay</u>.
It isn't my birthd<u>ay</u> 'til Saturd<u>ay</u>.
And as for the t<u>a</u>st<u>e</u>, well what can I s<u>ay</u>?
It's str<u>a</u>nge – but I'll eat it all up anyw<u>ay</u>."

# What do we mean by phonics?

Phonics is the name we give to the links between particular letter patterns in words and the sounds they represent. By drawing children's attention to these links, we provide them with tools to help them work out (or decode) words they have not met before. In other words, we are teaching them to read using phonics.

This is not the only approach to teaching reading, but it has been shown to be particularly helpful in the early stages of learning to read. While some children begin to make the link between sounds and letter patterns for themselves, many need to be taught this clearly. Some research findings suggest that progress in reading is faster when a phonic approach is used in the early stages.

# How can this book help?

Each of the books in this series has been designed to focus on a particular group of sounds and their related letter patterns. The rhymes in this book feature three long vowel sounds:

long *i* as in s<u>igh</u>, r<u>i</u>d<u>e</u>
long *u* as in gr<u>ew</u>, r<u>oo</u>m, f<u>u</u>m<u>e</u>
long *a* as in w<u>ai</u>t, pl<u>a</u>t<u>e</u>

The focus sound for each rhyme occurs repeatedly in words in that particular rhyme. The letters used to write the sounds are highlighted in each of those words. Long vowel sounds can be written with different patterns, depending on the word. These rhymes use words with the most common spelling patterns. As you share the rhymes with your child you will be helping them to make the vital link between particular letters and sounds.

# How should I use this book?

Children learn best when the experience is enjoyable. Read the rhymes to your child, sharing the pictures. Talk together about what happens in each rhyme. Now encourage your child to listen as you read the first rhyme again and to try to tell you which sound can be heard in lots of the words. Point out the highlighted sounds in the rhyme, explaining that these are the letters that we use to write the sounds. Help your child to read through the rhyme with you or to try to read it for him or herself.

Titles in the phonics range:

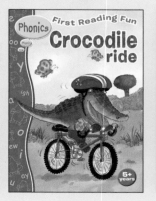